Improving
Writing

for ages 5–6

A & C Black • London

Contents

Introduction

Improving Writing presents a variety of stimulating activities to help pupils make progress with a wide range of writing skills.

So, what do we mean by 'improving writing'? Do we mean improving technical skills such as spelling, handwriting and punctuation? Or do we mean improving creative skills such as story-writing, descriptive work and poetry? The answer of course, is that we are seeking to improve a range of both technical and creative skills. This range is specified in the national guidelines for the assessment of writing, a summary of which is provided on page 4.

How to use this book

Each unit in this book features three worksheets at different levels to enable teachers to differentiate across the ability range. An animal picture at the top of the sheet indicates the level of the worksheet. The 'cat' exercises are at the simplest level; the 'dog' exercises are at the next level; the 'rabbit' exercises are at the most advanced level: Cat worksheets are for pupils working towards Level 1; Dog worksheets are for pupils working at Level 1; Rabbit worksheets are for pupils who are working confidently at Level 1 and are progressing towards Level 2. Each unit features a suggested learning objective and there is a class record sheet on page 64 to record progress.

Section 1 of this book features activities that are designed to **encourage pupils to write simple descriptive sentences**. Each activity consists of tasks appropriate to the three broad ability levels outlined above. Section 2 of this book features activities that are intended to guide pupils in **imaginative writing**.

How to use the CD-ROM

The accompanying CD-ROM contains printable and photocopiable PDFs of all the worksheets. All the photographs featured on the worksheets are also provided to enable you to display them in full colour on the whiteboard.

The guidelines for assessing writing

The guidelines for assessing writing at Level 1 suggest what the pupils should achieve 'in some writing, usually with support'. Note that each Assessment Focus has a sub-title that shows what pupils are working towards. In Assessment Focus 4, for example, the pupils are working towards 'constructing paragraphs and using cohesion within and between paragraphs' but the bullet points indicate that pupils at Level 1 are at the early stages of this process: we would not expect Year 1 pupils to write a text consisting of a set of well-structured paragraphs!

At the early stage of writing, pupils will be restricted by vocabulary to some extent. On pages 5 and 6 we list the vocabulary that is appropriate for each phase of 'Letters and Sounds'.

Guidelines for assessing writing at Level 1

You may wish to use this sheet as an individual record sheet by ticking the statements when you feel that pupils are secure in the specific skills that these represent.

Handwriting and presentation:
☐ Most letters are correctly formed and orientated.
☐ There are spaces between words.
☐ Upper and lower case letters are sometimes distinguished.
☐ ICT is used, eg for typing own name.

Assessment Focus 1 – write imaginative, interesting and thoughtful texts:
☐ Basic information and ideas are conveyed through appropriate word choice, eg related to a topic.
☐ Some descriptive language is used, eg colour, size, simple emotion.

Assessment Focus 2 – produce texts, which are appropriate to task, reader and purpose:
☐ There is some indication of basic purpose, particular form or awareness of reader, eg story, label, message.

Assessment Focus 3 – organise and present whole texts effectively, sequencing and structuring information, ideas and events:
☐ Some formulaic phrases indicate start/end of text, eg once upon a time, one day, the end.
☐ Events and ideas are sometimes in appropriate order, eg actions listed in time sequence, items numbered.

Assessment Focus 4 – construct paragraphs and use cohesion within and between paragraphs:
☐ Simple connections between ideas and events, eg repeated nouns, pronouns relate to main idea.

Assessment Focus 5 – vary sentences for clarity, purpose and effect:
☐ Reliance on simple phrases and clauses.
☐ Some sentence-like structures formed by chaining clauses together, eg series of ideas joined by repeated use of 'and'.

Assessment Focus 6 – write with technical accuracy of syntax and punctuation in phrases, clauses and sentences:
☐ Mostly grammatically accurate clauses.
☐ Some awareness of use of full stops and capital letters, eg beginning, end of sentence.

Assessment Focus 7 – select appropriate and effective vocabulary:
☐ Mostly simple vocabulary.
☐ Communicates meaning through repetition of key words.

Assessment Focus 8 – use correct spelling:
☐ Usually correct spelling of simple high frequency words.
☐ Phonetically plausible attempts at words with digraphs and double letters.
☐ Sufficient number of recognisable words for writing to be readable, including, eg use of letter names to approximate symbols and words.

Andrew Brodie: Improving Writing for ages 5–6 © A&C Black Publishers 2010

Vocabulary: Phases 2 and 3

We would expect Year 1 pupils to be working at Phases Two to Five of 'Letters and Sounds'.

The following vocabulary lists show the range of words likely to be used at each phase, though many pupils may well wish to use other words:

PHASE 2:
a an as at if in is it of off on up am
can dad had and get big him his not got mum but back

PHASE 3:
sat tap sit pit tip pip sip pan pin tin
nap man mat map dad sad dip did gap pig
dig pot top dog pop cot cap cat kid kit
sock sack dock pack pick pet ten net pen peg
men neck run mug cup sun mud rim rat hot
hut hop hum hit hat hug back bag bed bug
bun bus bat bin fit fin fun fog puff huff
cuff fan lap leg let bell fill doll tell sell
hill mill dull full less hiss mess boss fuss kiss
jam jet jog van vet win web wig wax wet
mix box six fox yes yet yell zip buzz quiz
chip chin check such much rich chill chap chick chat
ship shop shed shell fish dish wish rush shock cash
moth thin thick ring song wing rung king long sing
wait pain sail main tail rain feel feet jeep teeth
seem meet week deep keep high light might night tight
coat goat loaf road soap boat zoo boot zoom food
moon cool bar car bark card jar park fork sort
foot book cook good took hook born worn torn cork
burn curl hurt surf turn cow owl how town boil
coin soil ear hear near year hair fair sure cure
join gear pair pure hammer letter ladder dinner better summer

High frequency words
will that this then them with see for now down look too the to I
no go

PHASE 4:

CVCC words

tent	belt	hump	band	felt	gulp	lamp	wind	nest	sink
best	lift	lost	camp	kept	soft	pond	cost	bank	bunk
hand	next	milk	jump	melt	chest	chimp	bench	thank	shelf

CVCC and CCVC words

boost   paint   toast   think   burnt   stop   frog   spot   plan   trip

CCVC and CCV words

grab	track	spin	flag	twin	sniff	plum	swim	clap	drop
green	fresh	steep	tree	smell	train	spoon	sport	start	trail
cream	clown	star	creep	brown	spark	bring	crash	bleed	swing
float	smart	groan	brush	scoop	frown	droop	clear	growl	thrill

CCVCC, CCCVC and CCCVCC words

stand	crisp	spend	trust	twist	frost	stamp	blend	grunt	crept
slept	blink	drank	blank	trunk	crunch	shrink	spring	strap	street

Polysyllabic words

sandpit   windmill   softest   desktop   handstand   lunchbox   sandwich   thundering
starlight   floating   freshness   driftwood   twisting   printer   shampoo   chimpanzee

High frequency words

went   it's   from   children   just   help
he   she   we   me   be   was   my   you   her   they   all   are

PHASE 5:

horse   please   cheese   noise   because   done   nothing   brother   mother   happy
sunny   mummy   daddy   only   donkey   monkey   chimney   money   here   deer
cheer   steering   father   rather   half   calf   where   somewhere   everywhere   care
wear   tear   square   share   all   always   talk   walk   wall   fall   calling
four   your   fourteen   caught   taught   naughty   daughter   learn   earth   early
heard   word   work   world   worm   worse   worst   would   should   pull
push   full   play   spray   crayon   take   game   race   same   snake
sea   bead   read   steam   steamy   these   even   funny   quickly   field
try   tried   cry   cried   dry   dried   fry   fried   why   sky
slide   prize   nice   grow   snow   show   window   toe   goes   home
phone   woke   tune   use   huge   computer   few   new   blue   glue
June   rude   rule   blew   grew   screw   threw   sure   sugar   usual
picture   adventure   nature   mixture   catch   fetch   stitch   kitchen   fudge   hedge
bridge   badge   lamb   climb   crumb   thumb   gnome   sign   knot   knee
knock   know   knew   wrap   wrong   write   listen   castle   house   mouse

High frequency words

don't   old   I'm   by   time   house   about   your   day   made   came   make   here
saw   very   put   said   have   like   so   do   some   come   were   there   little   one
when   out   what   oh   their   people   Mr   Mrs   looked   called   asked   could   path
bath   ask   fast   last   daft   glass   grass   blast   afternoon

What can you see? 1

Name

Date

Word Bank   man   pig   pin   sock   peg   mug   bed   fox   fish

Look at the pictures. What can you see?

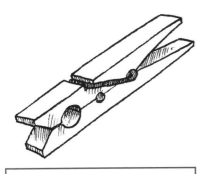

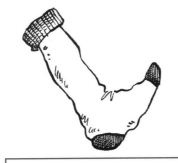

Name

Date

Word Bank   dog   sock   has   a   the   mat   and   wet

Look at the picture. What can you see?

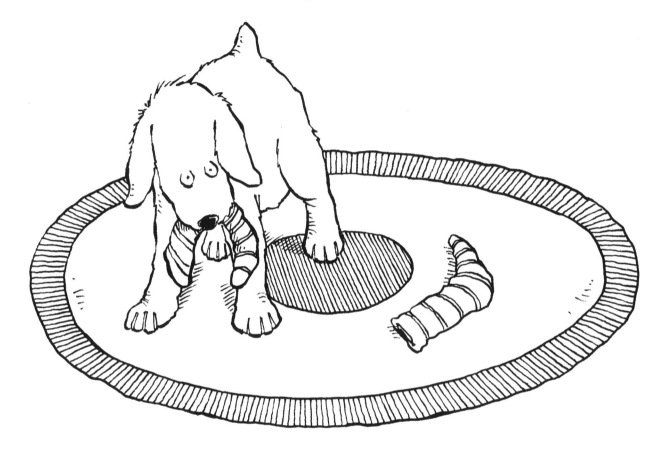

Teacher's Notes

This activity is suitable for children working at Phase Two or Phase Three.

Suggested objective: Write about the picture, choosing words carefully.
Read together: the instructions and the words in the word bank.
Talk together: Discuss the picture with the children. Can they describe what they see?
WOW (write own work): Support the child in writing a caption for the picture. Encourage the child to form their letters correctly and to leave appropriate spaces between words.
- Does the child convey basic information through appropriate word choice? (AF1)
- Does the child create an appropriate caption? (AF2)
- Does each child use correct spelling? (AF8)

What can you see? 1

Name

Date

Word Bank   man   dog   is   van   in   sits   the   mug

Look at the picture. What can you see?

Write about the picture.

What can you see? 2

Name

Date

bus   van   jam   box   shell   ship   shed   dish   moth

Look at the pictures. What can you see?

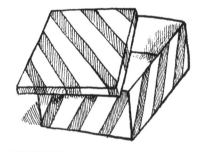

Teacher's Notes

This activity is suitable for children working at Phase Two or Phase Three.

Suggested objective: Write about the pictures, choosing words carefully.

Read together: the instructions and the words in the word bank

Talk together: Discuss the pictures with the children. Can they recognise each one?

WOW (write own work): Support the child in writing a label for each picture. Encourage the child to form their letters correctly.

● Does each child use correct spelling? (AF8)

● Does the child label each picture appropriately? (AF2)

What can you see? 2

Name

Date

Word Bank chips in dips jam king his the

Look at the picture. What can you see?

Teacher's Notes

This activity is suitable for children working at Phase Two or Phase Three.

Suggested objective: Write about the picture, choosing words carefully.

Read together: the instructions and the words in the word bank.

Talk together: Discuss the picture with the children. Can they describe what they see?

WOW (write own work): Support the child in writing a caption for the picture using words from the word bank. Encourage the child to form their letters correctly and to leave appropriate spaces between words.

● Does the child convey basic information through appropriate word choice? (AF1)

● Does the child create an appropriate caption? (AF2)

● Does each child use correct spelling? (AF8)

What can you see? 2

Name

Date

Word Bank   cook   book   looks   his   in   the   dinner   to

Look at the picture. What can you see?

Write about the picture.

What can you see? 3

Name

Date

Word Bank   boat   sail   tail   teeth   rain   coat   goat   moon   car

Look at the pictures. What can you see?

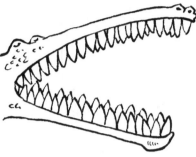

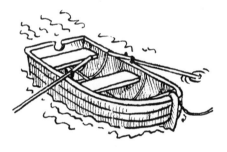

Teacher's Notes

This activity is suitable for children working at Phase Two or Phase Three.

Suggested objective: Write about the pictures, choosing words carefully.

Read together: the instructions and the words in the word bank.

Talk together: Discuss the pictures with the children. Can they recognise each one?

WOW (write own work): Support the child in writing a label for each picture. Encourage the child to form their letters correctly.

- Does each child use correct spelling? (AF8)
- Does the child label each picture appropriately? (AF2)

Name

Date

Word Bank boat sail rain coat goat on in a is has the

Look at the picture. What can you see?

Teacher's Notes

This activity is suitable for children working at Phase Two or Phase Three.

Suggested objective: Write about the picture, choosing words carefully.

Read together: the instructions and the words in the word bank.

Talk together: Discuss the picture with the children. Can they describe what they see?

WOW (write own work): Support the child in writing a caption for the picture using words from the word bank. Encourage the child to form their letters correctly and to leave appropriate spaces between words.

● Does the child convey basic information through appropriate word choice? (AF1)

● Does the child create an appropriate caption? (AF2)

● Does each child use correct spelling? (AF8)

What can you see? 3

Name

Date

Word Bank | owl cow tree moon a an asleep the is in dark night it

Look at the picture.
What can you see?

Write about the
picture.

Teacher's Notes

This activity is suitable for children working at Phase Four.

Suggested objective: Write about the picture, choosing words carefully.
Read together: the instructions and the words in the word bank.
Talk together: Discuss the picture with the children. Can they describe what they see?
WOW (write own work): Support the child in writing a caption for the picture, using words from the word bank.
Higher ability children may write one or more sentences. Encourage the child to form their letters correctly and
to leave appropriate spaces between words.
• Does the child convey basic information through appropriate word choice? (AF1)
• Does the child create an appropriate caption? (AF2)
• Does the child use some sentence-like structures? (AF5)
• Does the child show awareness of capital letters and full stops? (AF6)
• Does each child use correct spelling? (AF8)

Who is there?

Word Bank   cat   frog   dog   rat

Who is there?

A big, fat _____

Who is there?

A long, thin _____

Who is there?

A spotty _____

Who is there?

A big, green _____

Teacher's Notes

This activity is suitable for children working at Phase Two or Phase Three, but note that the word 'frog' is a CCVC word as seen in Phase Four.

Suggested objective: Complete the rhymes to interest the reader.
Read together: Discuss the rhyme with the children.
Talk together: Can they 'hear' which word should be written to complete the second and fourth verses?
WOW (write own work):
● Does each child show 'awareness of reader' and of rhyme form? (AF2)

Who is there?

Name

Date

Word Bank cat spotty frog long big thin dog rat fat

Who is there?

A big, fat _____

Who is there?

A long, thin _____

Who is there?

_____

Who is there?

_____

Teacher's Notes

This activity is suitable for children working at Phase Two or Phase Three, but note that the word 'frog' is a CCVC word as seen in Phase Four.

Suggested objective: Complete the rhymes to interest the reader.
Read together: Discuss the rhyme in the first two verses with the children.
Talk together: Can they 'hear' which word should be written to complete the second verse? Can they develop the rhyme form further by finding appropriate phrases to complete the third and fourth verses? Note that they may choose to use words that are not included in the word bank.
WOW (write own work):
● Does each child show 'awareness of reader' and of rhyme form? (AF2)
● Does the child use some descriptive language? (AF1)

Who is there?

Name

Date

Who is there?

A big, fat cat.

Who is there?

A long, thin rat.

Who is there?

Who is there?

Teacher's Notes

This activity is suitable for children working at Phase Two or Phase Three, but note that the word 'frog' is a CCVC word as seen in Phase Four.

Suggested objective: Complete the rhymes to interest the reader.

Read together: Discuss the rhyme in the first two verses with the children.

Talk together: Can they develop the rhyme form further by finding appropriate phrases to complete the third and fourth verses? Can they make up their own rhyme to create two extra verses? To give some clues, discuss the example picture of a rhyming pair. Encourage the children to think of descriptive words for each creature.

WOW (write own work):
- Does each child show 'awareness of reader' and of rhyme form? (AF2)
- Does the child use some descriptive language? (AF1)
- Does the child spell simple high frequency words correctly and are there enough recognizable words for the writing to be readable? (AF8)
- Does the child communicate meaning through repetition of key words? (AF7)

Hats

Word Bank   a   Mum   big   hat   has

Look at the picture.

Dad has a hat.

- -

Write about Mum.

- -

- -

- -

Teacher's Notes

This activity is suitable for children working at Phase Two, Phase Three or beyond.
Discuss the picture with the children. Can they compare Dad's hat to Mum's hat? Can they describe Mum's hat?

Suggested objective: Write about the picture, using sentences.
Read together: the short sentence about Dad's hat. Read together the words in the word bank.
Talk together: to make up a sentence about Mum's hat.
WOW (write own work): Support the child in writing a sentence about Mum's hat. Encourage the child to form their letters correctly and to use spaces between words.
● Is the child aware of the need for capital letters at the start of sentences and for 'Mum' and 'Dad'?
● Is the child aware of the need for a full stop at the end of each sentence? (AF6)

Hats

Name

Date

Word Bank a Mum big hat has Dad small

Look at the picture.

Write about the picture.

Teacher's Notes

This activity is suitable for children working at Phase Three, Phase Four or beyond.
Discuss the picture with the children. Can they compare Dad's hat to Mum's hat? Can they describe each hat?

Suggested objective: Write about the picture, using sentences.
Read together: the words in the word bank.
Talk together: to make up a sentence about Mum's hat and a sentence about Dad's hat.
WOW (write own work): Support the child in writing each sentence. Encourage the child to form their letters correctly and to use spaces between words.
● Is the child aware of the need for capital letters at the start of sentences and for 'Mum' and 'Dad'?
● Is the child aware of the need for a full stop at the end of each sentence? (AF6)

Andrew Brodie: Improving Writing for ages 5–6 © A&C Black Publishers 2010

Hats

Look at the picture.

Write about the picture.

Teacher's Notes

This activity is suitable for children working at Phase Three, Phase Four or beyond.
Discuss the picture with the children. Can they compare Dad's hat to Mum's hat? Can they describe each hat?

Suggested objective: Write about the picture, using sentences.
Talk together: to make up a sentence about Mum's hat and a sentence about Dad's hat. (AF4)
● Do they use the words 'spots' and 'stripes'? (AF1 and AF7)
WOW (write own work): Support the child in writing each sentence. Encourage the child to form their letters correctly and to use spaces between words.
● Is the child aware of the need for capital letters at the start of sentences and for 'Mum' and 'Dad'?
● Is the child aware of the need for a full stop at the end of each sentence? (AF6)
● Does the child spell simple high frequency words correctly and are there enough recognizable words for the writing to be readable? (AF8)

Name

Date

Word Bank hammer dinner ladder tent nest sink milk frog flag

Look at the pictures. What can you see?

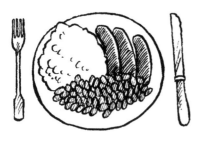

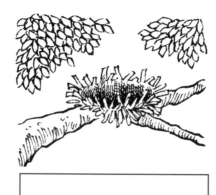

Teacher's Notes

This activity is suitable for children working at Phase Three or Phase Four.

Suggested objective: Write about the pictures, choosing words carefully.
Read together: the instructions and the words in the word bank.
Talk together: Discuss the pictures with the children. Can they recognise each one?
WOW (write own work): Support the child in writing a label for each picture. Encourage the child to form their letters correctly.

● Does each child use correct spelling? (AF8)
● Does the child label each picture appropriately? (AF2)

Name

Date

Word Bank toast toaster burnt the is in smoke bread loaf

Look at the picture. What can you see?

Teacher's Notes

This activity is suitable for children working at Phase Four or Phase Five.

Suggested objective: Write about the picture, choosing words carefully.
Read together: the instructions and the words in the word bank.
Talk together: Discuss the picture with the children. Can they describe what they see?
WOW (write own work): Support the child in writing a caption for the picture using words from the word bank.
Encourage the child to form their letters correctly and to leave appropriate spaces between words.

● Does the child convey basic information through appropriate word choice? (AF1)
● Does the child create an appropriate caption? (AF2)
● Does each child use correct spelling? (AF8)

Name

Date

| Word Bank | sad looks toast toaster burnt |
| | the is in smoke bread loaf man |

Look at the picture.
What can you see?

Write about the picture.

Teacher's Notes

This activity is suitable for children working at Phase Four or Phase Five.

Suggested objective: Write about the picture, choosing words carefully.
Read together: the instructions and the words in the word bank.
Talk together: Discuss the picture with the children. Can they describe what they see?
WOW (write own work): Support the child in writing a caption for the picture, using words from the word bank. Higher ability children may write one or more sentences. Encourage the child to form their letters correctly and to leave appropriate spaces between words.

- Does the child convey basic information through appropriate word choice? (AF1)
- Does the child create an appropriate caption? (AF2)
- Does the child use some sentence-like structures? (AF5)
- Does the child show awareness of capital letters and full stops? (AF6)
- Does each child use correct spelling? (AF8)

Andrew Brodie: Improving Writing for ages 5–6 © A&C Black Publishers 2010

Name

Date

Word Bank   windmill   handstand   lunchbox

horse   cheese   chimney   calf   square   worm

Look at the pictures. What can you see?

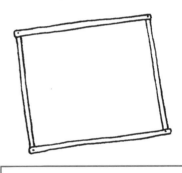

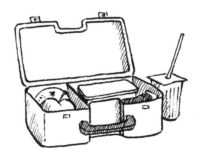

Teacher's Notes

This activity is suitable for children working at Phase Four or Phase Five.

Suggested objective: Write about the pictures, choosing words carefully.
Read together: the instructions and the words in the word bank.
Talk together: Discuss the pictures with the children. Can they recognise each one?
WOW (write own work): Support the child in writing a label for each picture. Encourage the child to form their letters correctly.

● Does each child use correct spelling? (AF8)
● Does the child label each picture appropriately? (AF2)

Andrew Brodie: Improving Writing for ages 5–6 © A&C Black Publishers 2010

Name

Date

Word Bank | chimpanzee sandpit does in handstand the

Look at the picture. What can you see?

Teacher's Notes

This activity is suitable for children working at Phase Four or Phase Five.

Suggested objective: Write about the picture, choosing words carefully.

Read together: the instructions and the words in the word bank.

Talk together: Discuss the picture with the children. Can they describe what they see?

WOW (write own work): Support the child in writing a caption for the picture using words from the word bank.
Encourage the child to form their letters correctly and to leave appropriate spaces between words.

● Does the child convey basic information through appropriate word choice? (AF1)
● Does the child create an appropriate caption? (AF2)
● Does each child use correct spelling? (AF8)

What can you see? 5

Name

Date

Word Bank at horse same the a donkey race time finished and had they

Look at the picture.
What can you see?

Write about the picture.

Teacher's Notes

This activity is suitable for children working at Phase Five.

Suggested objective: Write about the picture, choosing words carefully.
Read together: the instructions and the words in the word bank.
Talk together: Discuss the picture with the children. Can they describe what they see?
WOW (write own work): Support the child in writing a caption for the picture, using words from the word bank.
Higher ability children may write one or more sentences or they may use the connective 'and' to join clauses
together. Encourage the child to form their letters correctly and to leave appropriate spaces between words.
● Does the child convey basic information through appropriate word choice? (AF1)
● Does the child create an appropriate caption? (AF2)
● Does the child use some sentence-like structures? (AF5)
● Does the child show awareness of capital letters and full stops? (AF6)
● Does each child use correct spelling? (AF8)

Where is the cat?

Name

Date

Word Bank | a   post   cat   on   A

Look at the picture.

Write about the picture.

Teacher's Notes

This picture is available on the CD and can be viewed on the whiteboard.
This activity is suitable for children working at Phase Two or Phase Three.

Suggested objective: Write about the picture, using sentences.
Read together: the instructions on the sheet and the words in the word bank.
Talk together: Discuss the picture with the children. What can the child tell you about the cat? Encourage each child to write a simple sentence, such as 'A cat is on a post.'
WOW (write own work):
- Does the child show some indication of basic purpose? (AF2)
- Is the child aware of the need for a full stop at the end of each sentence? (AF6)

Andrew Brodie: Improving Writing for ages 5–6 © A&C Black Publishers 2010

Where is the cat?

Name

Date

Word Bank a post cat tail black white the

Look at the picture.

Write about the picture.

Teacher's Notes

This picture is available on the CD and can be viewed on the whiteboard.
This activity is suitable for children working at Phase Four.

Suggested objective: Write about the picture, using sentences.
Read together: the instructions on the sheet and the words in the word bank.
Talk together: Discuss the picture with the children. What can the child tell you about the cat? Encourage each child to compose a simple sentence, such as 'A cat is on a post' but also to add further detail, perhaps in a second sentence, eg 'The cat is black and white'.
WOW (write own work):
● Does the child show some indication of basic purpose? (AF2)
● Does the child convey basic information and ideas? (AF1)
● Does the child show simple connections between ideas? (AF4)
● Does the child write some sentence-like structures? (AF5)
● Is the child aware of the need for a full stop at the end of each sentence? (AF6)
● Does the child use correct spelling? (AF8)

Where is the cat?

Name

Date

Word Bank a post cat tail blue black
white the fence field sky jump ground

Look at the picture.

Write about the picture.

Teacher's Notes

This picture is available on the CD and can be viewed on the whiteboard.
This activity is suitable for children working at Phase Four or beyond.

Suggested objective: Write about the picture, using sentences.
Read together: the instructions on the sheet and the words in the word bank.
Talk together: Discuss the picture with the children. What can the child tell you about the cat? Encourage
each child to compose some sentences about the picture.
WOW (write own work):
● Does the child show some indication of basic purpose? (AF2)
● Does the child convey basic information and ideas? (AF1)
● Does the child show simple connections between ideas? (AF4)
● Does the child write some sentence-like structures? (AF5)
● Is the child aware of the need for a full stop at the end of each sentence? (AF6)
● Does the child use correct spelling? (AF8)

Andrew Brodie: Improving Writing for ages 5–6 © A&C Black Publishers 2010

Where is the frog?

Name

Date

Word Bank   frog   grass   hat   green   on   the   a

Look at the picture.

Write about the picture.

- -

- -

- -

Teacher's Notes

This picture is available on the CD and can be viewed on the whiteboard.
This activity is suitable for children working at Phase Three, Phase Four or beyond.

Suggested objective: Write about the picture, using sentences.
Read together: the instructions on the sheet and the words in the word bank.
Talk together: Discuss the picture with the children. What can the child tell you about the frog? Encourage each child to write a simple sentence, such as 'A frog is on a hat.'
WOW (write own work):
- Does the child show some indication of basic purpose? (AF2)
- Is the child aware of the need for a full stop at the end of each sentence? (AF6)

Andrew Brodie: Improving Writing for ages 5–6 © A&C Black Publishers 2010

Where is the frog?

Word Bank frog grass hat green on the a ground upside down

Look at the picture.

Write about the picture.

Teacher's Notes

This picture is available on the CD and can be viewed on the whiteboard.
This activity is suitable for children working at Phase Four or beyond.

Suggested objective: Write about the picture, using sentences.
Read together: the instructions on the sheet and the words in the word bank.
Talk together: Discuss the picture with the children. What can the child tell you about the frog? Encourage each child to compose a simple sentence, such as 'A frog is on a hat' but also to add further detail, perhaps in a second sentence, eg 'The frog is green.'
WOW (write own work):
- Does the child show some indication of basic purpose? (AF2)
- Does the child convey basic information and ideas? (AF1)
- Does the child show simple connections between ideas? (AF4)
- Does the child write some sentence-like structures? (AF5)
- Is the child aware of the need for a full stop at the end of each sentence? (AF6)
- Does the child use correct spelling? (AF8)

Where is the frog?

Name

Date

Word Bank frog grass hat green on the a ground upside down pattern

Look at the picture.

Write about the picture.

What can you see? 6

Name

Date

Word Bank   half   walk   fall   daughter   world
snake   steam   slide   window

Look at the pictures. What can you see?

Name
Date

Word Bank   children   field   race   quickly   ran   the   a   they

Look at the picture. What can you see?

Teacher's Notes

This activity is suitable for children working at Phase Five or beyond.

Suggested objective: Write about the picture, choosing words carefully.
Read together: the instructions and the words in the word bank.
Talk together: Discuss the picture with the children. Can they describe what they see?
WOW (write own work): Support the child in writing a caption for the picture using words from the word bank.
Some children may be able to write one or more sentences. Encourage the child to form their letters correctly
and to leave appropriate spaces between words.
● Does the child convey basic information through appropriate word choice? (AF1)
● Does the child create an appropriate caption? (AF2)
● Does each child use correct spelling? (AF8)

Name

Date

Word Bank troll under over on hiding billy-goat
field grass bridge across went was the eat to some

Look at the picture.
What can you see?

Write about the picture.

Teacher's Notes

This activity is suitable for children working at Phase Five or beyond.

Suggested objective: Write about the picture, choosing words carefully.

Read together: the instructions and the words in the word bank.

Talk together: Discuss the picture with the children. Can they describe what they see?

WOW (write own work): Support the child in writing a caption for the picture, using words from the word bank.
Higher ability children may write one or more sentences or they may use the connective 'and' to join clauses
together. Encourage the child to form their letters correctly and to leave appropriate spaces between words.

● Does the child convey basic information through appropriate word choice? (AF1)
● Does the child create an appropriate caption? (AF2)
● Does the child use some sentence-like structures? (AF5)
● Does the child show awareness of capital letters and full stops? (AF6)
● Does each child use correct spelling? (AF8)

                    Andrew Brodie: Improving Writing for ages 5–6 © A&C Black Publishers 2010

A moth

Name

Date

Word Bank   moth   yellow   black   white   orange   on   the   a   this   is

Look at the picture.

Write about the picture.

Teacher's Notes

This picture is available on the CD and can be viewed on the whiteboard.
This activity is suitable for children working at Phase Three, Phase Four or beyond.

Suggested objective: Write about the picture, using sentences.
Read together: the instructions on the sheet and the words in the word bank.
Talk together: Discuss the picture with the children. What can the child tell you about the moth? Encourage each child to write a simple sentence, such as 'This is a moth' or 'The moth is black and white and yellow.'
WOW (write own work):
● Does the child convey basic information through appropriate word choice? (AF1)
● Does the child show some indication of basic purpose? (AF2)
● Is the child aware of the need for a capital letter at the start and a full stop at the end of each sentence? (AF6)
● Does the child use correct spelling? (AF8)

A moth

Name

Date

Word Bank moth yellow black white orange on the a wall stone

Look at the picture.

Write about the picture.

Teacher's Notes

This picture is available on the CD and can be viewed on the whiteboard.
This activity is suitable for children working at Phase Four or beyond.

Suggested objective: Write about the picture, using sentences.
Read together: the instructions on the sheet and the words in the word bank.
Talk together: Discuss the picture with the children. What can the child tell you about the moth? Encourage each child to compose a simple sentence, such as 'The moth is on a wall' but also to add further detail, perhaps in a second sentence, eg 'The moth is black and white and yellow.'
WOW (write own work):
● Does the child show some indication of basic purpose? (AF2)
● Does the child convey basic information and ideas? (AF1)
● Does the child show simple connections between ideas? (AF4)
● Does the child write some sentence-like structures? (AF5)
● Is the child aware of the need for a capital letter at the start and a full stop at the end of each sentence? (AF6)
● Does the child use correct spelling? (AF8)

                    Andrew Brodie: Improving Writing for ages 5–6 © A&C Black Publishers 2010

A moth

Name

Date

Word Bank | moth yellow black white orange on the a wall stone

Look at the picture.

Write about the picture.

Teacher's Notes

This picture is available on the CD and can be viewed on the whiteboard.
This activity is suitable for children working at Phase Four or beyond.

Suggested objective: Write about the picture, using sentences.
Read together: the instructions on the sheet and the words in the word bank.
Talk together: Discuss the picture with the children. What can the child tell you about the moth? Encourage each child to compose some sentences about the picture.
WOW (write own work):
● Does the child show some indication of basic purpose? (AF2)
● Does the child convey basic information and ideas? (AF1)
● Does the child show simple connections between ideas? (AF4)
● Does the child write some sentence-like structures? (AF5)
● Is the child aware of the need for a capital letter at the start and a full stop at the end of each sentence? (AF6)
● Does the child use correct spelling? (AF8)

Tall tree

Name

Date

Word Bank   tall   tree   the   a   this   is   picture   very

Look at the picture.

Write about the picture.

Teacher's Notes

This picture is available on the CD and can be viewed on the whiteboard.
This activity is suitable for children working at Phase Five.

Suggested objective: Write about the picture, using sentences.
Read together: the instructions on the sheet and the words in the word bank.
Talk together: Discuss the picture with the children. What can the child tell you about the tree and its surroundings? Encourage each child to write a simple sentence, such as 'This is a tall tree' or 'This tree is very tall.'
WOW (write own work):
● Does the child convey basic information through appropriate word choice? (AF1)
● Does the child show some indication of basic purpose? (AF2)
● Is the child aware of the need for a capital letter at the start and a full stop at the end of each sentence? (AF6)
● Does the child use correct spelling? (AF8)

Andrew Brodie: Improving Writing for ages 5–6 © A&C Black Publishers 2010

Tall tree

Name

Date

Word Bank tall tree fence gate there hedge hedges by field fields the a this is picture very near

Look at the picture.

Write about the picture.

Teacher's Notes

This picture is available on the CD and can be viewed on the whiteboard.
This activity is suitable for children working at Phase Five or beyond.

Suggested objective: Write about the picture, using sentences.
Read together: the instructions on the sheet and the words in the word bank.
Talk together: Discuss the picture with the children. What can the child tell you about the tree and its surroundings? Encourage each child to compose a simple sentence, such as 'This is a tall tree' but also to add further detail, perhaps in a second sentence, eg 'The tree is near a gate.'
WOW (write own work):
● Does the child show some indication of basic purpose? (AF2)
● Does the child convey basic information and ideas? (AF1)
● Does the child show simple connections between ideas? (AF4)
● Does the child write some sentence-like structures? (AF5)
● Is the child aware of the need for a capital letter at the start and a full stop at the end of each sentence? (AF6)
● Does the child use correct spelling? (AF8)

Tall tree

Name

Date

Look at the picture.

Write about the picture.

Days of the week

Read about my week.

On Monday I come to school.
On Tuesday I go swimming.
On Wednesday I visit my friend.
On Thursday I have chips for tea.
On Friday I play on the computer.
On Saturday I go shopping.
On Sunday I stay in bed quite late!

Write about what you do on some days.

On Monday I ....

....

On Friday I ....

....

On Saturday I ....

....

On Sunday I ....

....

Teacher's Notes

This activity is suitable for children working at Phase Five or beyond.

Suggested objective: Write about things that happen on different days.

Read together: the instructions and the sentences.

Talk together: Discuss the days of the week with the children, encouraging them to remember what they do each day. Ask each child to think especially about what they do on Monday, Friday, Saturday and Sunday.

WOW (write own work): Support the child in completing each sentence. Encourage the child to form their letters correctly.

- Does the child convey basic information through appropriate word choice? (AF1)
- Does the child show some indication of basic purpose? (AF2)
- Are events and ideas presented in appropriate order? (AF3)
- Does the child make simple connections between ideas and events? (AF4)
- Is the child aware of the need for a capital letter at the start and a full stop at the end of each sentence? (AF6)
- Does the child use correct spelling? (AF8)

Name

Date

Read about my week.

On Monday I come to school.

On Tuesday I go swimming.

On Wednesday I visit my friend.

On Thursday I have chips for tea.

On Friday I play on the computer.

On Saturday I go shopping.

On Sunday I stay in bed quite late!

Write about what you do on some days.

Teacher's Notes

This activity is suitable for children working at Phase Five or beyond.

Suggested objective: Write about things that happen on different days.

Read together: the instructions and the sentences.

Talk together: Discuss the days of the week with the children, encouraging them to remember what they do each day. Ask each child to think about days when something special happens. Help them to compose some sentences orally

WOW (write own work): Support the child in writing at least one sentence. Encourage the child to form their letters correctly and to leave appropriate spaces between words.

- Does the child convey basic information through appropriate word choice? (AF1)
- Does the child show some indication of basic purpose? (AF2)
- Are events and ideas presented in appropriate order? (AF3)
- Does the child make simple connections between ideas and events? (AF4)
- Is the child aware of the need for a capital letter at the start and a full stop at the end of each sentence? (AF6)
- Does the child select appropriate and effective vocabulary? (AF7)
- Does the child use correct spelling? (AF8)

Days of the week

Name

Date

Read about my week.

On Monday I come to school
early in the morning.
After school I go swimming.
In the evening I watch television.

Write about what you do on one day of the week.

Teacher's Notes

This activity is suitable for children working at Phase Five or beyond.

Suggested objective: Write about things that happen on different days.

Read together: the instructions and the sentences. Encourage the children to notice the time clues in the sentences, ie 'on Monday', 'early in the morning', 'after school', 'in the evening'.

Talk together: Discuss the days of the week with the children, encouraging them to remember what they do each day. Ask each child to think about a day when something special happens. Help them to compose some sentences orally.

WOW (write own work): Support the child in writing at least one sentence. Encourage the child to form their letters correctly and to leave appropriate spaces between words.

- Does the child convey basic information through appropriate word choice? (AF1)
- Does the child show some indication of basic purpose? (AF2)
- Are events and ideas presented in appropriate order? (AF3)
- Does the child make simple connections between ideas and events? (AF4)
- Does the child vary sentences for clarity, purpose and effect? (AF5)
- Is the child aware of the need for a capital letter at the start and a full stop at the end of each sentence? (AF6)
- Does the child select appropriate and effective vocabulary? (AF7)
- Does the child use correct spelling? (AF8)

My house

Word Bank house flat bungalow mobile home caravan
road town village city country big small little it is

Read about my house.

My house is in a village.
It is a small house.

Write about your home.

Teacher's Notes

This activity is suitable for children working at Phase Five or beyond.

Suggested objective: Describe your home, choosing good words for your sentences.
Read together: the word bank, the instructions and the sentences.
Talk together: Discuss the children's homes with them – do they live in any of the types listed in the word bank? If not, write the name of the appropriate type of home. Ask each child to compose a sentence about her/his own home.
WOW (write own work): Support the child in writing their sentence. Encourage the child to form their letters correctly and to leave appropriate gaps between words.
- Does the child convey basic information through appropriate word choice? (AF1)
- Does the child show some indication of basic purpose? (AF2)
- Are events and ideas presented in appropriate order? (AF3)
- Does the child make simple connections between ideas and events? (AF4)
- Is the child aware of the need for a capital letter at the start and a full stop at the end of each sentence? (AF6)
- Does the child select appropriate and effective vocabulary? (AF7)
- Does the child use correct spelling? (AF8)

    Andrew Brodie: Improving Writing for ages 5–6 © A&C Black Publishers 2010

My house

Name

Date

house flat bungalow mobile home caravan road town village city country garden

Read about my house.

My house is in a village.
It is a small house.
There is a tree in the garden.

Write about your home.

Teacher's Notes

This activity is suitable for children working at Phase Five or beyond.

Suggested objective: Describe your home, choosing good words for your sentences.

Read together: the word bank, the instructions and the sentences.

Talk together: Discuss the children's homes with them – do they live in any of the types listed in the word bank? If not, write the name of the appropriate type of home. Ask each child to compose at least one sentence about her/his own home.

WOW (write own work): Support the child in writing their sentences. Encourage the child to form their letters correctly and to leave appropriate gaps between words.

● Does the child convey basic information through appropriate word choice? (AF1)
● Does the child show some indication of basic purpose? (AF2)
● Are events and ideas presented in appropriate order? (AF3)
● Does the child make simple connections between ideas and events? (AF4)
● Is the child aware of the need for a capital letter at the start and a full stop at the end of each sentence? (AF6)
● Does the child select appropriate and effective vocabulary? (AF7)
● Does the child use correct spelling? (AF8)

My house

Name

Date

Read about my house.

My house is in a village.
The house is small but
there is a big garden.
There is a tree in the
garden.

Write about your home.

Teacher's Notes

This activity is suitable for children working at Phase Five or beyond.

Suggested objective: Describe your home, choosing good words for your sentences.

Read together: the instructions and the sentences. Discuss the second sentence, pointing out the connective 'but'.

Talk together: Discuss the children's homes with them – do they live in any of the types listed in the word bank? If not, write the name of the appropriate type of home. Ask each child to compose at least one sentence about her/his own home.

WOW (write own work): Support the child in writing their sentences. Encourage the child to form their letters correctly and to leave appropriate gaps between words.

- Does the child convey basic information through appropriate word choice? (AF1)
- Does the child show some indication of basic purpose? (AF2)
- Are events and ideas presented in appropriate order? (AF3)
- Does the child make simple connections between ideas and events? (AF4)
- Is the child aware of the need for a capital letter at the start and a full stop at the end of each sentence? (AF6)
- Does the child select appropriate and effective vocabulary? (AF7)
- Does the child use correct spelling? (AF8)

My pet

Name

Date

Word Bank   mouse   cat   dog   budgie   tortoise
horse   guinea-pig   rabbit   goldfish

Read about my hamster.

I have a pet hamster.
I love my hamster.

Write about a pet.

Teacher's Notes

This activity is suitable for children working at Phase Five or beyond.

Suggested objective: Describe a pet, choosing good words for your sentences.
Read together: the word bank, the instructions and the sentences.
Talk together: Discuss the children's pets with them – do they all have pets? If not, discuss what pet they might like or what pet a friend or relation has. Ask each child to compose a sentence about a pet.
WOW (write own work): Support the child in writing their sentence. Encourage the child to form their letters correctly and to leave appropriate gaps between words.
● Does the child convey basic information through appropriate word choice? (AF1)
● Does the child show some indication of basic purpose? (AF2)
● Are events and ideas presented in appropriate order? (AF3)
● Does the child make simple connections between ideas and events? (AF4)
● Is the child aware of the need for a capital letter at the start and a full stop at the end of each sentence? (AF6)
● Does the child select appropriate and effective vocabulary? (AF7)
● Does the child use correct spelling? (AF8)

My pet

Name

Date

budgie   tortoise   horse   guinea-pig   goldfish

Read about my hamster.

I have a pet hamster.
My hamster is called Rory.

Write about a pet.

Teacher's Notes

This activity is suitable for children working at Phase Five or beyond.

Suggested objective: Describe a pet, choosing good words for your sentences.

Read together: the word bank, the instructions and the sentences.

Talk together: Discuss the children's pets with them – do they all have pets? If not, discuss what pet they might like or what pet a friend or relation has. Ask each child to compose at least one sentence about a pet.

WOW (write own work): Support the child in writing their sentences. Encourage the child to form their letters correctly and to leave appropriate gaps between words.

- Does the child convey basic information through appropriate word choice? (AF1)
- Does the child show some indication of basic purpose? (AF2)
- Are events and ideas presented in appropriate order? (AF3)
- Does the child make simple connections between ideas and events? (AF4)
- Is the child aware of the need for a capital letter at the start and a full stop at the end of each sentence? (AF6)
- Does the child select appropriate and effective vocabulary? (AF7)
- Does the child use correct spelling? (AF8)

My pet

Name

Date

Read about my hamster.

I have a pet hamster and he is called Rory. He plays on a wheel in his cage.

Write about a pet.

Teacher's Notes

This activity is suitable for children working at Phase Five or beyond.

Suggested objective: Describe a pet, choosing good words for your sentences.
Read together: the instructions and the sentences. Point out the connective 'and' in the first sentence.
Talk together: Discuss the children's pets with them – do they all have pets? If not, discuss what pet they might like or what pet a friend or relation has. Ask each child to compose at least two sentences about a pet.
WOW (write own work): Support the child in writing their sentences. Encourage the child to form their letters correctly and to leave appropriate gaps between words.

- Does the child convey basic information through appropriate word choice? (AF1)
- Does the child show some indication of basic purpose? (AF2)
- Are events and ideas presented in appropriate order? (AF3)
- Does the child make simple connections between ideas and events? (AF4)
- Is the child aware of the need for a capital letter at the start and a full stop at the end of each sentence? (AF6)
- Does the child select appropriate and effective vocabulary? (AF7)
- Does the child use correct spelling? (AF8)

Snowman

Name

Date

Word Bank   snowman   a   this   is   picture   very   snow   scarf
hat   coal   mouth   nose   eyes   legs   arms   cold   winter

Look at the picture.

Write about the picture.

Teacher's Notes

This picture is available on the CD and can be viewed on the whiteboard.
This activity is suitable for children working at Phase Five or beyond.

Suggested objective: Describe the snowman, choosing good words for your sentences.
Read together: the instructions on the sheet and the words in the word bank.
Talk together: Discuss the picture with the children. What can the child tell you about the snowman and what he is wearing? Encourage each child to write a simple sentence, such as 'This is a snowman' or 'This is a picture of a snowman.'
WOW (write own work):
● Does the child convey basic information through appropriate word choice? (AF1)
● Does the child show some indication of basic purpose? (AF2)
● Is the child aware of the need for a capital letter at the start and a full stop at the end of each sentence? (AF6)
● Does the child select appropriate and effective vocabulary? (AF7)
● Does the child use correct spelling? (AF8)

Andrew Brodie: Improving Writing for ages 5–6 © A&C Black Publishers 2010

Snowman

Name

Date

Word Bank snowman picture very snow scarf coal
mouth eyes cold winter

Look at the picture.

Write about the picture.

Teacher's Notes

This picture is available on the CD and can be viewed on the whiteboard.
This activity is suitable for children working at Phase Five or beyond.

Suggested objective: Describe the snowman, choosing good words for your sentences.
Read together: the instructions on the sheet and the words in the word bank.
Talk together: Discuss the picture with the children. What can the child tell you about the snowman and what he is wearing? Encourage each child to compose a simple sentence, such as 'This is a snowman' but also to add further detail, perhaps in a second sentence, eg 'He is wearing a scarf and a hat.'
WOW (write own work):
• Does the child show some indication of basic purpose? (AF2)
• Does the child convey basic information and ideas? (AF1)
• Does the child show simple connections between ideas? (AF4)
• Does the child write some sentence-like structures? (AF5)
• Is the child aware of the need for a capital letter at the start and a full stop at the end of each sentence? (AF6)
• Does the child select appropriate and effective vocabulary? (AF7)
• Does the child use correct spelling? (AF8)

Snowman

Name

Date

Look at the picture.

Write about the picture.

Teacher's Notes

This picture is available on the CD and can be viewed on the whiteboard.
This activity is suitable for children working at Phase Five or beyond.

Suggested objective: Describe the snowman, choosing good words for your sentences.
Read together: the instructions on the sheet.
Talk together: Discuss the picture with the children. What can the child tell you about the snowman? Note that there is no word bank to give clues and you may need to prompt the children with some ideas. Encourage each child to compose some sentences about the picture.
WOW (write own work):
- Does the child show some indication of basic purpose? (AF2)
- Does the child convey basic information and ideas? (AF1)
- Does the child organise and present texts effectively? (AF3)
- Does the child show simple connections between ideas? (AF4)
- Does the child write some sentence-like structures? (AF5)
- Is the child aware of the need for a capital letter at the start and a full stop at the end of each sentence? (AF6)
- Does the child select appropriate and effective vocabulary? (AF7)
- Does the child use correct spelling? (AF8)

Andrew Brodie: Improving Writing for ages 5–6 © A&C Black Publishers 2010

Apple blossom

Name

Date

Word Bank   apple blossom   leaves   tree   flowers

pink   white   red   blue   there   are   growing   spring

Look at the picture.

Write about the picture.

Teacher's Notes

This picture is available on the CD and can be viewed on the whiteboard.
This activity is suitable for children working at Phase Five or beyond.

Suggested objective: Write about spring flowers, choosing good words for your sentences.
Read together: the instructions on the sheet and the words in the word bank.
Talk together: Discuss the picture with the children. What can the child tell you about the flowers? Encourage each child to write a simple sentence, such as 'This is apple blossom' or 'The flowers are growing on a tree.''
WOW (write own work):
- Does the child convey basic information through appropriate word choice? (AF1)
- Does the child show some indication of basic purpose? (AF2)
- Is the child aware of the need for a capital letter at the start and a full stop at the end of each sentence? (AF6)
- Does the child select appropriate and effective vocabulary? (AF7)
- Does the child use correct spelling? (AF8)

Apple blossom

Name

Date

apple blossom   leaves   flowers   growing   spring

Look at the picture.

Write about the picture.

Teacher's Notes

This picture is available on the CD and can be viewed on the whiteboard.
This activity is suitable for children working at Phase Five or beyond.

Suggested objective: Write about spring flowers, choosing good words for your sentences.
Read together: the instructions on the sheet and the words in the word bank.
Talk together: Discuss the picture with the children. What can the child tell you about the flowers? What can you tell them about the flowers? Encourage each child to compose a simple sentence, such as 'This is apple blossom' but also to add further detail, perhaps in a second sentence, eg 'It is spring time.'
WOW (write own work):
- Does the child show some indication of basic purpose? (AF2)
- Does the child convey basic information and ideas? (AF1)
- Does the child show simple connections between ideas? (AF4)
- Does the child write some sentence-like structures? (AF5)
- Is the child aware of the need for a capital letter at the start and a full stop at the end of each sentence? (AF6)
- Does the child select appropriate and effective vocabulary? (AF7)
- Does the child use correct spelling? (AF8)

Apple blossom

Name

Date

Look at the picture.

Write about the picture.

Teacher's Notes

This picture is available on the CD and can be viewed on the whiteboard.
This activity is suitable for children working at Phase Five or beyond.

Suggested objective: Write about spring flowers, choosing good words for your sentences.
Read together: the instructions on the sheet.
Talk together: Discuss the picture with the children. What can the child tell you about the apple blossom?
Note that there is no word bank to give clues and you may need to prompt the children with some ideas about
spring growth. Encourage each child to compose some sentences about the picture.
WOW (write own work):
- Does the child show some indication of basic purpose? (AF2)
- Does the child convey basic information and ideas? (AF1)
- Does the child organise and present texts effectively? (AF3)
- Does the child show simple connections between ideas? (AF4)
- Does the child write some sentence-like structures? (AF5)
- Is the child aware of the need for a capital letter at the start and a full stop at the end of each sentence? (AF6)
- Does the child select appropriate and effective vocabulary? (AF7)
- Does the child use correct spelling? (AF8)

Name

Date

Word Bank beach people colours sea sand red blue yellow purple orange playing paddling sunbathing summer hot warm

Look at the picture.

Write about the picture.

Teacher's Notes

This picture is available on the CD and can be viewed on the whiteboard.
This activity is suitable for children working at Phase Five or beyond.

Suggested objective: Write about the beach, choosing good words for your sentences.
Read together: the instructions on the sheet and the words in the word bank.
Talk together: Discuss the picture with the children. What can the child tell you about the beach? Encourage each child to write a simple sentence, such as 'This is a beach' or 'The people are on the beach.'
WOW (write own work):
● Does the child convey basic information through appropriate word choice? (AF1)
● Does the child show some indication of basic purpose? (AF2)
● Is the child aware of the need for a capital letter at the start and a full stop at the end of each sentence? (AF6)
● Does the child select appropriate and effective vocabulary? (AF7)
● Does the child use correct spelling? (AF8)

Andrew Brodie: Improving Writing for ages 5–6 © A&C Black Publishers 2010

Beach

Name

Date

beach people colours sea sand red blue yellow purple orange playing paddling sunbathing summer hot warm

Look at the picture.

Write about the picture.

Teacher's Notes

This picture is available on the CD and can be viewed on the whiteboard.
This activity is suitable for children working at Phase Five or beyond.

Suggested objective: Write about the beach, choosing good words for your sentences.
Read together: the instructions on the sheet and the words in the word bank.
Talk together: Discuss the picture with the children. What can the child tell you about the beach? Encourage each child to compose a simple sentence, such as 'This is a beach' but also to add a second sentence, eg 'It is summer time' and perhaps a third sentence, eg 'The people are playing in the sunshine.'
WOW (write own work):
● Does the child show some indication of basic purpose? (AF2)
● Does the child convey basic information and ideas? (AF1)
● Does the child show simple connections between ideas? (AF4)
● Does the child write some sentence-like structures? (AF5)
● Is the child aware of the need for a capital letter at the start and a full stop at the end of each sentence? (AF6)
● Does the child select appropriate and effective vocabulary? (AF7)
● Does the child use correct spelling? (AF8)

Beach

Look at the picture.

Write about the picture.

Teacher's Notes

This picture is available on the CD and can be viewed on the whiteboard.
This activity is suitable for children working at Phase Five or beyond.

Suggested objective: Write about the beach, choosing good words for your sentences.
Read together: the instructions on the sheet.
Talk together: Discuss the picture with the children. What can the child tell you about the beach? Note that there is no word bank to give clues and you may need to prompt the children with some ideas about summer. Encourage each child to compose some sentences about the picture.
WOW (write own work):
- Does the child show some indication of basic purpose? (AF2)
- Does the child convey basic information and ideas? (AF1)
- Does the child organise and present texts effectively? (AF3)
- Does the child show simple connections between ideas? (AF4)
- Does the child write some sentence-like structures? (AF5)
- Is the child aware of the need for a capital letter at the start and a full stop at the end of each sentence? (AF6)
- Does the child select appropriate and effective vocabulary? (AF7)
- Does the child use correct spelling? (AF8)

Autumn tree

Name

Date

Look at the picture.

Write about the picture.

Teacher's Notes

This picture is available on the CD and can be viewed on the whiteboard.
This activity is suitable for children working at Phase Five or beyond.

Suggested objective: Write about the autumn tree, choosing good words for your sentences.
Read together: the instructions on the sheet and the words in the word bank.
Talk together: Discuss the picture with the children. What can the child tell you about the tree? Encourage
each child to write a simple sentence, such as 'This is a tree in autumn' or 'The leaves have turned brown.'
WOW (write own work):
● Does the child convey basic information through appropriate word choice? (AF1)
● Does the child show some indication of basic purpose? (AF2)
● Is the child aware of the need for a capital letter at the start and a full stop at the end of each sentence? (AF6)
● Does the child select appropriate and effective vocabulary? (AF7)
● Does the child use correct spelling? (AF8)

Autumn tree

Name

Date

leaves   orange   autumn   turned   have   brown

Look at the picture.

Write about the picture.

Teacher's Notes

This picture is available on the CD and can be viewed on the whiteboard.
This activity is suitable for children working at Phase Five or beyond.

Suggested objective: Write about the autumn tree, choosing good words for your sentences.
Read together: the instructions on the sheet and the words in the word bank.
Talk together: Discuss the picture with the children. What can the child tell you about the leaves on the tree?
Encourage each child to compose a simple sentence, such as 'This is a tree in autumn' but also to add a second
sentence, eg 'The leaves have turned brown' and perhaps a third sentence, eg 'The leaves will fall off the tree.'
WOW (write own work):
● Does the child show some indication of basic purpose? (AF2)
● Does the child convey basic information and ideas? (AF1)
● Does the child show simple connections between ideas? (AF4)
● Does the child write some sentence-like structures? (AF5)
● Is the child aware of the need for a capital letter at the start and a full stop at the end of each sentence? (AF6)
● Does the child select appropriate and effective vocabulary? (AF7)
● Does the child use correct spelling? (AF8)

Andrew Brodie: Improving Writing for ages 5–6 © A&C Black Publishers 2010

Autumn tree

Name

Date

Look at the picture.

Write about the picture.

Teacher's Notes

This picture is available on the CD and can be viewed on the whiteboard.
This activity is suitable for children working at Phase Five or beyond.

Suggested objective: Write about the autumn tree, choosing good words for your sentences.
Read together: the instructions on the sheet.
Talk together: Discuss the picture with the children. What can the child tell you about the tree? Note that there is no word bank to give clues and you may need to prompt the children with some ideas about autumn. Encourage each child to compose some sentences about the picture.
WOW (write own work):
● Does the child show some indication of basic purpose? (AF2)
● Does the child convey basic information and ideas? (AF1)
● Does the child organise and present texts effectively? (AF3)
● Does the child show simple connections between ideas? (AF4)
● Does the child write some sentence-like structures? (AF5)
● Is the child aware of the need for a capital letter at the start and a full stop at the end of each sentence? (AF6)
● Does the child select appropriate and effective vocabulary? (AF7)
● Does the child use correct spelling? (AF8)

Class record sheet

You may find it helpful to record which sheets each child has completed. You could use a green pen to record 'Rabbit' worksheets, an orange pen to record 'Dog' worksheets and a red pen to record 'Cat' worksheets.

Name

Name	What can you see? 1	What can you see? 2	What can you see? 3	Who is there?	Hats	What can you see? 4	What can you see? 5	Where is the cat?	Where is the frog?	What can you see? 6	A moth	Tall tree	Days of the week	My house	My pet	Snowman	Apple blossom	Beach	Autumn tree

Andrew Brodie: Improving Writing for ages 5–6 © A&C Black Publishers 2010